What was that? He couldn't believe it! Without thinking, he snatched one item with his teeth.

Since he couldn't open the outside __ __ __ __ , he
                                            10
checked behind all the curtains until he found a

__ __ __ __ __ __ that was open. He then jumped into
  3
the backyard with his loot.

Where should he hide it? He saw the perfect spot beneath

an old elm __ __ __ __ . Quickly, Max dug a hole with his
              12

__ __ __ __ .
 8

The evidence was hidden, but now Max must face the

family and accept the consequences of his caper.

"I'm not sure I like this life of crime," thought Max.

What did Max take?

__   __ __ __ __   __ __ __ __   __ __ __ __
 1   2 3 4 5   6 7 8   9 10 11 12

SHEAR CALAMITY

How many things can you find wrong in this barbershop?

MALL MAZE

Marla and her brother Judson have been at the mall all day. Now they need to find the quickest way back to the front door so they can meet their mom for a ride home.

START

NO EXIT

FINISH

Answer on page 47.

LET'S CELEBRATE!

Look at the picture clues below. Write the names of the holidays associated with each picture in the spaces on the next page.

ACROSS

DOWN

5.

1.

8.

2.

3.

9.

4.

10.

6.

15.

7.

12.

11.

16.

17.

13.

14.

Illustrated by R. Michael Palan

Answer on page 47.

DINNER PARTY

These pictures are out of order. Can you number
them to show what happened first, second, and so on?

 Answer on page 47.

DOT MAGIC

Ahoy, there! Connect these dots to find out what is
sailing over the bounding main.

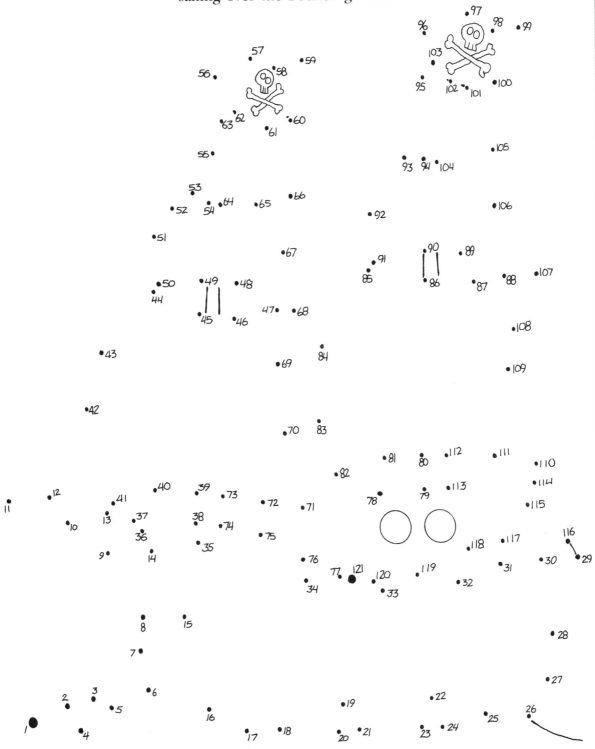

GLOBE PROBE

That famous explorer, Cincinnati Holmes, has travelled all over the world. He's learned about many different cultures and languages. Listed on this page are eight different sets of words that Cincy knows. Your job is to match each language with one of the countries where it is spoken, and then help Cincy find that country on his big map.

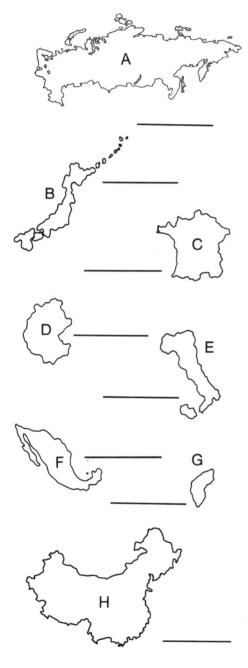

Illustrated by John Nez

HELLO	GOODBYE	THANK YOU	LANGUAGE
1. Bon jour	Au revoir	Merci	French
2. Guten tag	Auf wiedersehen	Danke	German
3. Bon giorno	Addio	Grazie	Italian
4. Buenos dias	Adios	Gracias	Spanish
5. Ohio	Sayonara	Kansha suru	Japanese
6. Nihow	Tzay-jiann	Shieh-shieh	Chinese
7. Shalom	Lihitraot	Todah	Hebrew
8. Strasvitziya	Dosvidanya	Spacebo	Russian

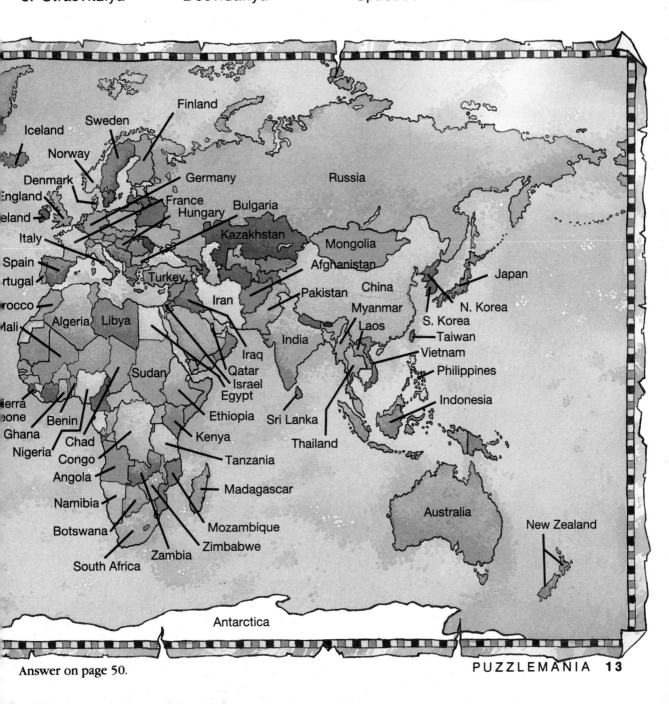

WHO HOOKED THE HORSESHOE?

Here's one school of fish that has learned to outsmart the opposition. Can you tell whose fishing line has hooked an unexpected catch?

Answer on page 47.

14

STOCK CAR MEMORIES

Part 1

Take a long look at this picture. Try to remember everything you see in it. Then turn the page, and try to answer some questions about it without looking back.

STOCK CA

LAP 9

START TIME

DON'T READ THIS UNTIL YOU HAVE LOOKED AT "Stock Car Memories—Part 1" ON PAGE 15.

STOCK CAR MEMORIES   Part 2

Can you answer these questions about the stock car scene you saw? Don't peek!

1. What was the number on the car in the lead?
2. What color flag was the track man waving?
3. How many cars were in the race?
4. How many red barrels are standing on the side?
5. What lap of the race was being run?
6. What was in the mechanic's back pocket?
7. How many loudspeakers were on the poles?
8. What color was the lead car?

Answer on page 47.

RIDDLE OF THE PYRAMID

Given the numbers below to start off, can you figure out how to reach the mystery number at the top of this pyramid? Each empty box contains the sum of the two numbers beneath it on either corner. One example 1+2=3 is already done to show you how this all adds up.

Illustrated by Rob Sepanak

Answer on page 48.

IN THE BATH

Some items found in your bathroom are listed below. See if you can fit them all into the spaces. Each word is used only once, so cross it off the list when you've found the spot for it. We've done the first one for you.

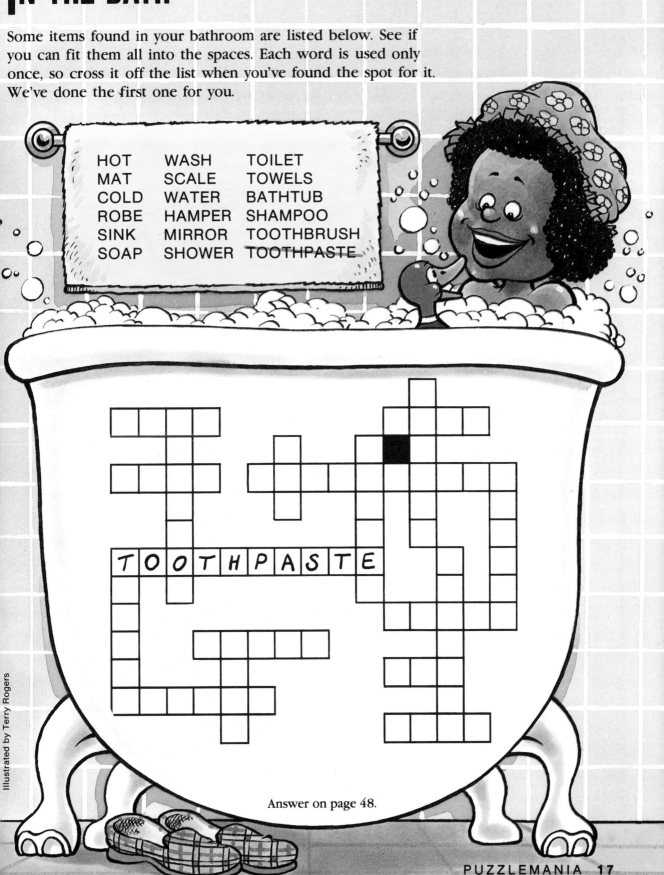

HOT   WASH   TOILET
MAT   SCALE   TOWELS
COLD   WATER   BATHTUB
ROBE   HAMPER   SHAMPOO
SINK   MIRROR   TOOTHBRUSH
SOAP   SHOWER   TOOTHPASTE

TOOTHPASTE

Answer on page 48.

Illustrated by Terry Rogers

HIDDEN PICTURES

There are at least 20 objects hidden in this picture.
How many can you find?

ODD ONE OUT

In each group of four words, only three things belong together. Can you figure out what each group is and which word doesn't belong with the others?

1. Taco - Lasagna - Burrito - Enchilada

2. Biology - Physics - Chemistry - History

3. Gallon - Celsius - Kilometer - Gram

4. Potato - Carrot - Lettuce - Radish

5. Ottawa - Saskatchewan - New Brunswick - Manitoba

6. Mississippi - Erie - Rio Grande - Colorado

7. Angola - Botswana - Ethiopia - Paraguay

8. Bowling - Football - Tennis - Ice Hockey

Illustrated by John Nez

Answer on page 48.

INSTANT PICTURE

Hidden on this page is something that makes your home look neat and keeps baseball fields ready for play. To find out what it is, fill in each section containing two dots.

Illustrated by Rob Sepanak

FLAG FUN

Semaphore is a method of sending messages over great distances by using flags. It was once popular on ships and with the Boy Scouts. Use the semaphore alphabet shown below to decode the message on the next page.

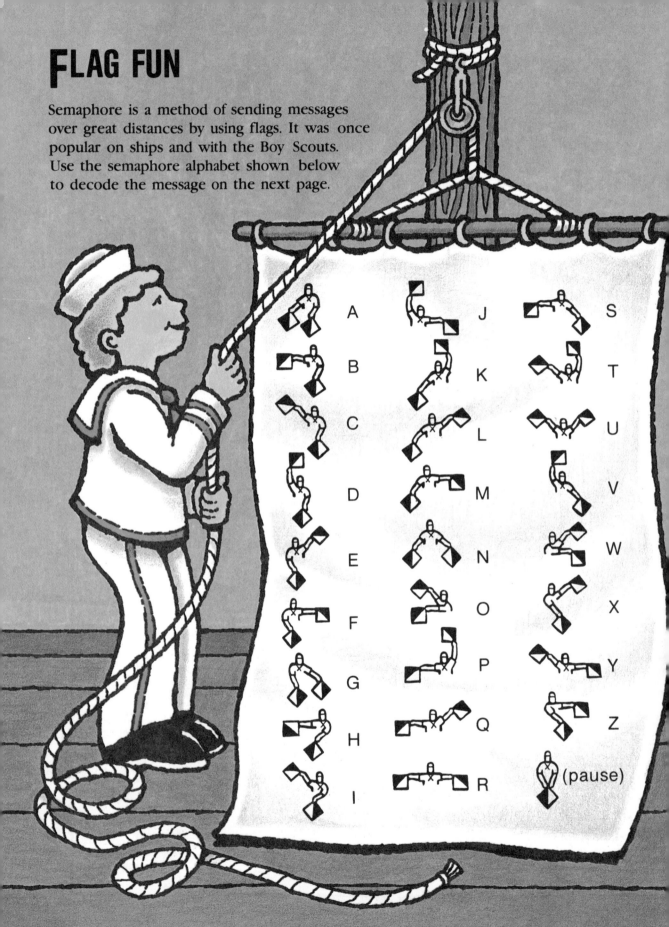

Illustrated by R. Michael Palan

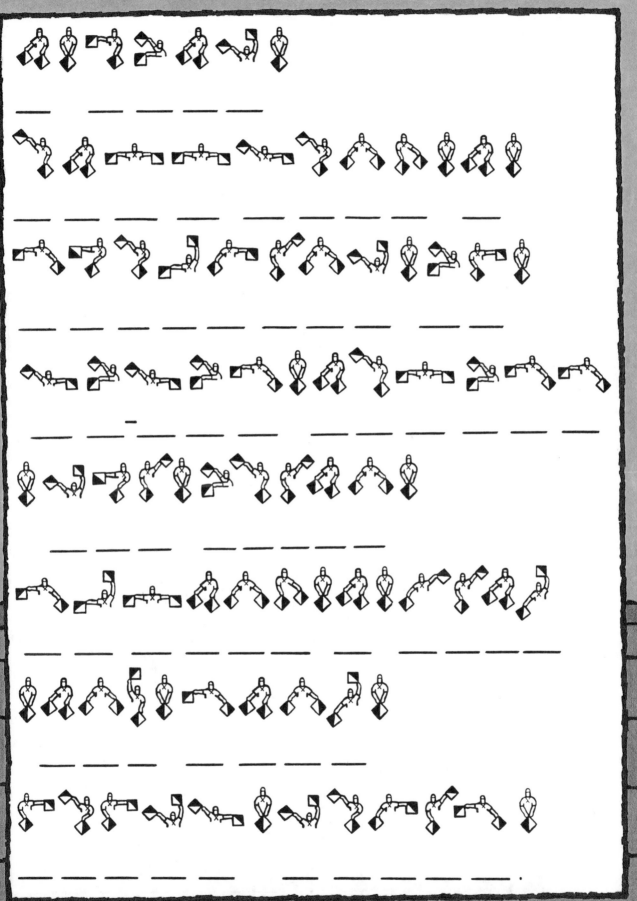

Answer on page 48.

GOBLETY GOOK

A goblet is a cup for drinking. There are at least 25 goblets hidden in this picture. How many can you find?

PLANE THINKING

Quincy and three other friends joined the local Model Airplane Club. When they attended their first meeting each brought a model airplane made from a different material. From the clues below, can you determine the first and last name of each child, and what each airplane was made from? Use the chart to keep track of the facts. Put an X in a square that can't be true, and an O in a square that is definitely yes. For example, clue 5 says Patty is not the Smith child. Find the column where Patty and Smith meet. Since that information doesn't match, put an X in that box.

	Bibb	Cole	Ladd	Smith	Styro.	Balsa	Plastic	Paper
Quincy								
Patty								
Rita								
Sam								

1. Patty, who is not the Ladd child, did not bring the styrofoam airplane.
2. The Smith child's airplane was made of balsa wood.
3. Sam Cole admired Quincy's plastic airplane.
4. The Bibb child made a paper airplane.
5. Patty is not the Smith child.

Answer on page 48.

Illustrated by Terry Burton

ANIMAL ANATOMY

Many animals have the names of different parts of the human body hidden in their own names. Some of these animals are pictured on the next page. Match each animal with the correct line. The yellow boxes show where a body part appears in each animal's name. When you've figured out which body part goes where, put all the same letters on spaces with matching numbers. Use the chart for clues about different parts of the body.

1. __ __ __ __ __
   9 1 2 3 4

2. __ __ __ __ __ __ __ __ __   __ __ __ __ __
   5 2 10 10 6 15 5 6 2 7   9 5 2 15 17

3. __ __ __ __ __ __ - __ __ __ __   __ __ __ __ __ __ __
   16 8 12 12 4 6   1 8 9 6   7 8 4 14 5 3 1

4. __ __ __ __ __ __ __ __ __ __   __ __ __ __
   9 10 2 4 4 10 8 11 12 5   16 2 9 9

5. __ __ __ __ __ __ __ __ __ __
   13 5 3 1 13 5 3 4 4 2

6. __ __ __ __ __ __ __ __ __
   2 15 10 2 7 3 4 4 8

7. __ __ __ __ __ __ __ __   __ __ __ __ __
   5 11 10 14 16 2 13 17   19 5 2 4 6

8. __ __ __ __ __ __ __
   13 2 15 3 16 8 11

9. __ __ __ __ __ __ __ __ __ __ __ __
   5 3 14 14 8 14 8 12 2 10 11 9

10. __ __ __ __
   13 2 4 18

11. __ __ __ __ __ - __ __ __ __ __ __   __ __ __ __ __ __
   16 4 2 13 17   18 8 8 12 6 7   18 6 15 15 6 12

12. __ __ __ __ __ - __ __ __ __   __ __ __ __ __
   12 5 15 6 6   12 8 6 7   9 4 8 12 5

Answer on page 48.

NUMBERS, PLEASE

Each paragraph below comes with three numbers and three blanks. Fit the numbers into the proper blanks so that the paragraphs make sense.

A.   12   8   10
Jack is _____ . His older brother Frank is _____ , and Linda, the baby of the family, is _____ .

B. $2.00 $6.00 $9.98
Carl gets _____ a week allowance. The toy he wants costs _____ . So far he hasn't spent any of his money and has saved _____ .

C.   180   9   36
Mr. James wears a size _____ suit and a size _____ shoe. He weighs _____ pounds.

D.   46   23   38
On January _____ , 1988, I was _____ inches tall. Today I am almost _____ inches tall.

E.   45   350   8
The recipe says to bake the cake in an _____-inch pan for _____ minutes at _____ degrees.

F.   70   90   100
I got _____ on my first two spelling tests this month, but last week my score dropped to _____ . Now my average is _____ .

G.   20   120   140
Mrs. Brown weighed _____ pounds when she got married. Now she weighs _____ pounds. Her goal is to lose those extra _____ pounds.

Illustrated by Paul Richer

Answer on page 48.

STOP, LOOK, AND LIST

Under each category, list one thing that begins with every letter. For example, one weather word that begins with "D" is Damp. See if you can name another.

WEATHER WORDS

D _____

S _____

C _____

M _____

T _____

THINGS BABIES NEED

D _____

S _____

C _____

M _____

T _____

MATH WORDS

D _____

S _____

C _____

M _____

T _____

Illustrated by Lisa Dayer

Answer on page 49.

LOOKING AROUND THE LIBRARY

Look around the letters on the next page. Forty-two words that have to do with going to the library are hidden there. Look up, down, across, backward, and diagonally to find them all.

art	fines	place
atlas	history	poetry
audiotape	idea	quiet
author	index	quotes
biography	library	reading
books	listening	romance
classic	magazines	science
cover	marker	shelf
dictionary	music	stories
dreaming	newspapers	table
encyclopedia	nonfiction	textbooks
enjoyment	novels	thesaurus
fantasy	pages	tome
fiction	paper	word

Illustrated by Barbara Gray

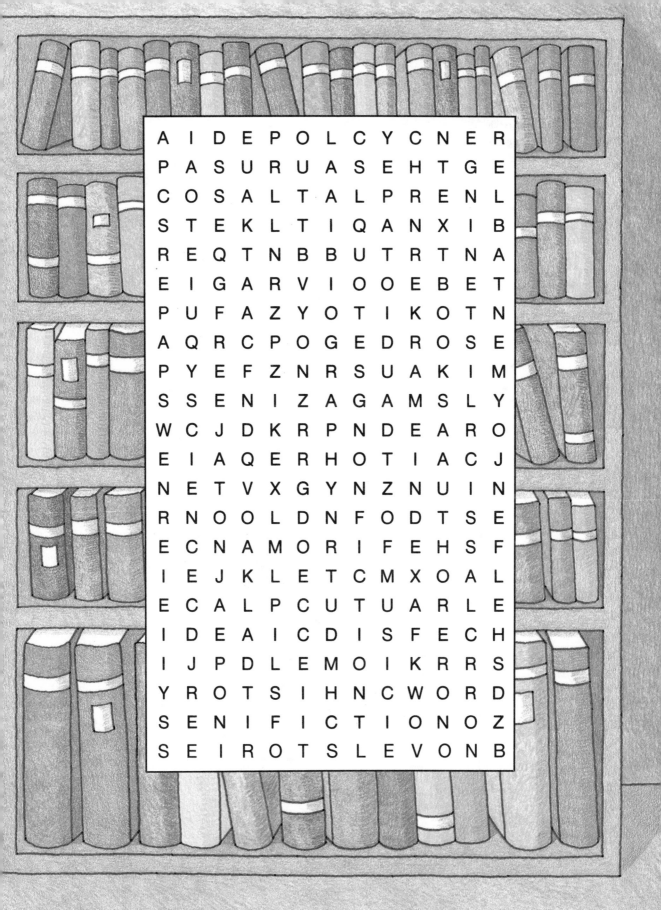

A I D E P O L C Y C N E R
P A S U R U A S E H T G E
C O S A L T A L P R E N L
S T E K L T I Q A N X I B
R E Q T N B B U T R T N A
E I G A R V I O O E B E T
P U F A Z Y O T I K O T N
A Q R C P O G E D R O S E
P Y E F Z N R S U A K I M
S S E N I Z A G A M S L Y
W C J D K R P N D E A R O
E I A Q E R H O T I A C J
N E T V X G Y N Z N U I N
R N O O L D N F O D T S E
E C N A M O R I F E H S F
I E J K L E T C M X O A L
E C A L P C U T U A R L E
I D E A I C D I S F E C H
I J P D L E M O I K R R S
Y R O T S I H N C W O R D
S E N I F I C T I O N O Z
S E I R O T S L E V O N B

ORSE SENSE

Can you tell which aquarium Shadow the seahorse lives in? She lives with five fish, one of which is striped, and no other sea horses. There is a castle in her aquarium, too.

Answer on page 49.

Illustrated by Terry Rogers

WHAT'S IN A WORD?

The word SATELLITE contains many smaller words. SAT and TELL are two that are easy to find. There are at least twenty-five other words of three letters or more orbiting around here. How many words can you find in SATELLITE?

Answer on page 49.

PICTURE MIXER

Copy these mixed-up squares in the spaces on the next page to put this picture back together. The letters and numbers tell you where each square belongs. The first one, A-3, has been done for you.

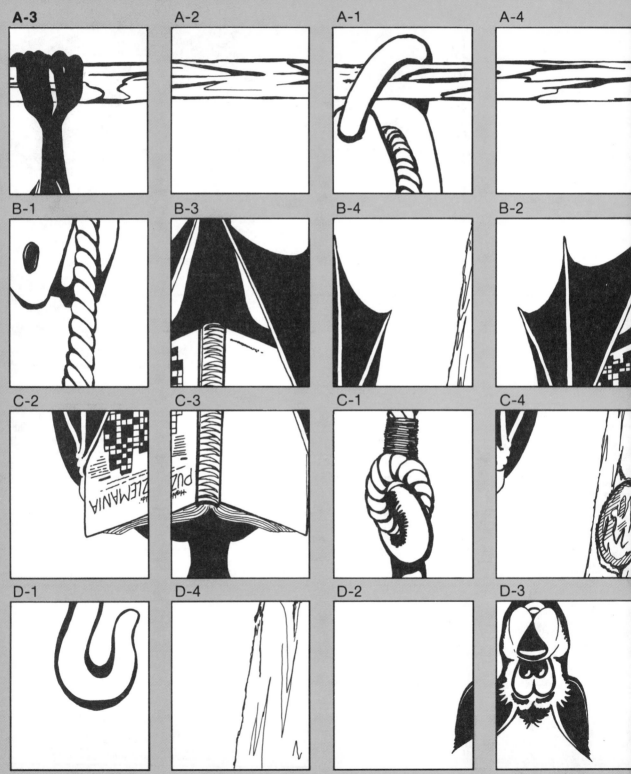

Illustrated by Rob Sepanak

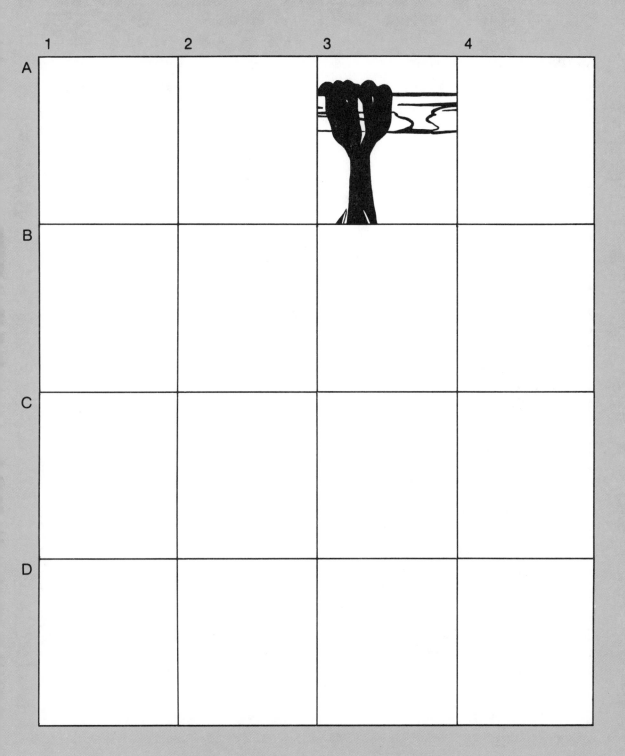

JUST J

Jump right in to find all the things that begin with the letter J.

Illustrated by Lynn Adams

LAST CHANCE WITH "ANCE"

Each of these words ends with "ance." To figure out what comes in advance, give the clues a glance.

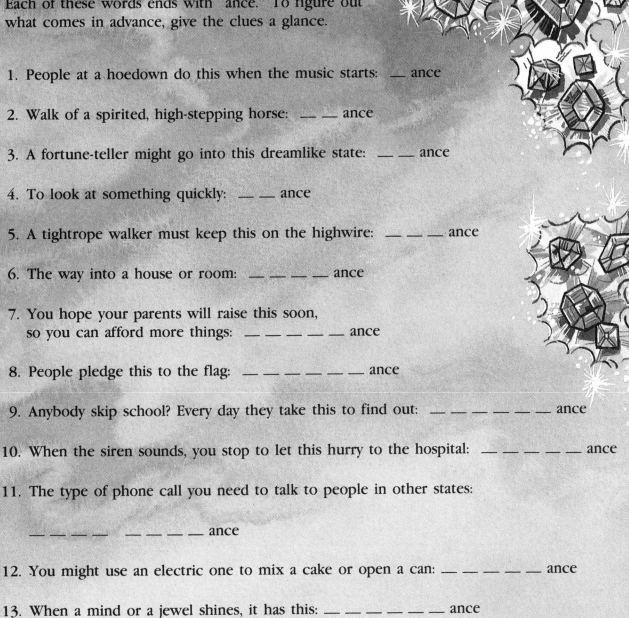

1. People at a hoedown do this when the music starts: __ ance

2. Walk of a spirited, high-stepping horse: __ __ ance

3. A fortune-teller might go into this dreamlike state: __ __ ance

4. To look at something quickly: __ __ ance

5. A tightrope walker must keep this on the highwire: __ __ __ ance

6. The way into a house or room: __ __ __ __ ance

7. You hope your parents will raise this soon,
   so you can afford more things: __ __ __ __ __ ance

8. People pledge this to the flag: __ __ __ __ __ __ ance

9. Anybody skip school? Every day they take this to find out: __ __ __ __ __ __ ance

10. When the siren sounds, you stop to let this hurry to the hospital: __ __ __ __ __ ance

11. The type of phone call you need to talk to people in other states:

    __ __ __ __   __ __ __ __ ance

12. You might use an electric one to mix a cake or open a can: __ __ __ __ __ __ ance

13. When a mind or a jewel shines, it has this: __ __ __ __ __ __ ance

14. "Auld Lang Syne" asks if this old thing may be forgot: __ __ __ __ __ __ __ ance

Answer on page 49.

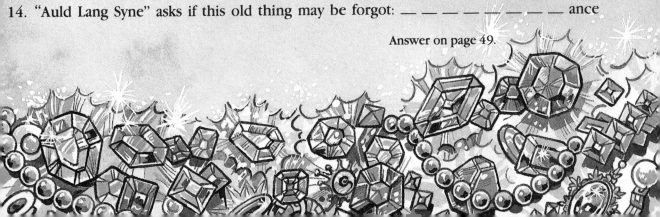

WHAT AM I?

I have a flat, broad, paddle-like tail;
  Through the water I can swiftly sail.
My strong teeth help me cut branches and trees;
  I work very hard building lodges with these.
What am I?

1. My first letter is in bean but not mean.

2. The second can be found in eagle twice.

3. Letter three is in seam but not seem.

4. The next is in vice but not mice.

5. The fifth letter is in glue and shoe.

6. My last letter is in robin and true.

— — — — — —
1 2 3 4 5 6

Answer on page 49.

RAT RACER

Help Roger race through this maze to his hole. Be quick, before Snowball wakes up.

Answer on page 49.

FINISH

Illustrated by Charles Jordan

START

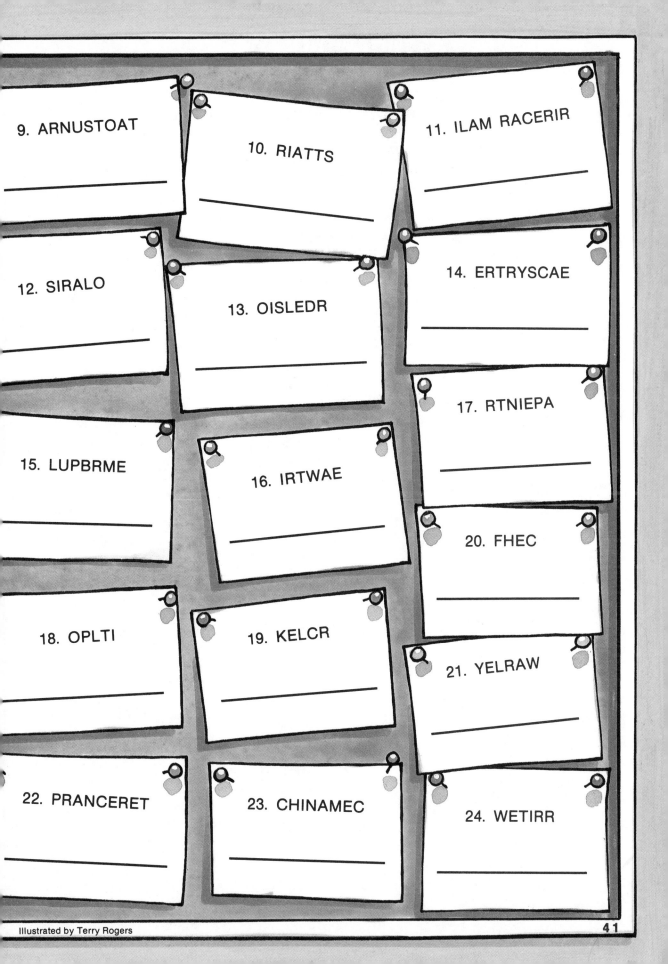

ROW, ROW, ROW

It's Manny Monster's birthday and all of his friends have gathered for a party. Each of these monsters has something in common with the two other monsters in the same row. For example, all of the monsters in the top row across have two triangular fangs. Look at the other rows across, down, and diagonally. What's the same about each row of three?

Illustrated by Lynn Adams

Answer on page 50.

IN THE CENTER RING

The Bumbling Brothers Circus is introducing their newest performer in the center ring. Is it a moose juggling derbies while riding a unicycle? Or maybe it's a squirrel who's doing loop-the-loops through the trapeze. Use your imagination to draw in whatever you think is in the spotlight.

MUSIC, MUSIC

There's a lot of noise coming off these pages because of all the instruments gathered here. Not all the questions are about music, but sound out as many as you can. Use the clues below to fill in the grid on the next page.

ACROSS

1. A brass trumpet-like instrument
5. Another instrument, the French ___
8. Feed for horses
9. A low-pitched brass instrument that makes "oompah" sounds
10. Anger
11. Human beings
13. An abbreviation used instead of Miss or Mrs.
14. Mother
15. The short form of a stringed instrument popular in Hawaii
16. A loud noise or racket
17. Me, ___self and I
18. The seventh tone of the musical scale
19. When the band plays "The Star Spangled Banner" we ___ ___ . (2 words)
21. 2,000 pounds
22. Minerals or rocks containing valuable metals
23. East-northeast (abbreviation)
24. An item in the mouthpiece of a clarinet
25. A public road in the city

DOWN

1. Ringing percussion instruments
2. Items used to propel a rowboat
3. A grain used to make dark bread
4. Increases in size
5. An Eskimo dog
6. A woodwind instrument
7. Moved rapidly
9. A brass instrument, or the sound an elephant makes
12. A small piano
14. Dug for gold
16. Challenge someone
18. A vocal or musical sound
20. Part of the foot
21. A golfer hits the ball off a ___

Answer on page 50.

WAYS TO GO

Various methods of transportation are hidden in the sentences below. They will be in two or more words with the letters in sequence and not jumbled. Take a look at the example below, get going!

Example: Are you goin*g on Dola*'s boat next week? The word gondola, which is a type of boat, is hidden in three words.

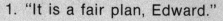

1. "It is a fair plan, Edward."
2. The girl's hip and hand were broken in the accident.
3. The order of garlic arrived too late for the party.
4. Here's the weather report: rain and gusty winds.
5. You could sell both or sell one.
6. "Put rucksacks in the back," the driver said.
7. We'll meet Bobo at the circus.
8. Grab all Oona's sheets off the rack.
9. Of all the family, Greg Liderman was the last to arrive.
10. Didn't Carri age well after all these years?

Answer on page 50.

ANSWERS

TREASURE TROVE (page 3)
F is the matching pot of gold.

THE CASE OF THE CANINE CROOK (pages 4-5)

This is the sad story of Max, who couldn't resist temptation. Max was a small brown DOG with a huge bark, soft brown EYES, and a TAIL that wagged a lot. He belonged to Joe Chandler, a 10-year-old BOY who loved him very much. Max lived with Joe and his family in a small gray HOUSE.

One day when the family was not at HOME, Max, who was very bored, looked about for something to do.

Mrs. Chandler had left some packages on the kitchen TABLE, and Max decided to investigate. He sniffed at all the items with his sensitive NOSE.

What was that? He couldn't believe it! Without thinking, he snatched one item with his teeth.

Since he couldn't open the outside DOOR, he checked behind all the curtains until he found a WINDOW that was open. He then jumped into the backyard with his loot.

Where should he hide it? He saw the perfect spot beneath an old elm TREE. Quickly, Max dug a hole with his PAWS.

The evidence was hidden, but now Max must face the family and accept the consequences of his caper.

"I'm not sure I like this life of crime," thought Max.

What did Max take?

A	B	I	G	S	O	U	P	B	O	N	E
1	2	3	4	5	6	7	8	9	10	11	12

MALL MAZE (page 7)

LET'S CELEBRATE! (pages 8-9)

DINNER PARTY (page 10)

6   4
1   3
2   5

DOT MAGIC (page 11)

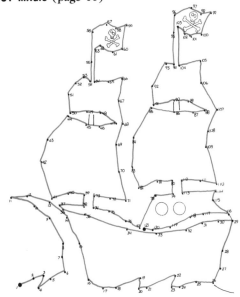

GLOBE PROBE (pages 12-13)
This answer appears on page 50.

WHO HOOKED THE HORSESHOE? (page 14)
The young man on the right has the horseshoe.

STOCK CAR MEMORIES (page 16)

1. 17	3. Six	5. Nine	7. Two
2. Yellow	4. Three	6. A hammer	8. Yellow

RIDDLE OF THE PYRAMID (page 16)

IN THE BATH (page 17)

ODD ONE OUT (page 20)

1. Lasagna (the others are all Mexican foods; lasagna is Italian)
2. History (the others are sciences)
3. Gallon (the others are metric measurements)
4. Lettuce (the others are root crops; lettuce grows above ground)
5. Ottawa (the others are Canadian provinces; Ottawa is a city)
6. Erie (the others are rivers; Erie is a lake)
7. Paraguay (the others are nations in Africa; Paraguay is in South America)
8. Ice Hockey (the others are sports that use a ball; ice hockey requires a puck)

INSTANT PICTURE (page 21)

FLAG FUN (pages 22-23)

A BOAT CARRYING A SHIPMENT OF YO-YOS ACROSS THE OCEAN SPRANG A LEAK AND SANK FIFTY TIMES

PLANE THINKING (page 25)

Patty is not the Cole or Ladd child (clue 1), nor is she the Smith child (clue 5); Patty is the Bibb child. Her airplane was not made of styrofoam or plastic (clue 1) or balsa wood (clue 2). Her airplane was made from paper (clue 4).

Sam Cole (clue 3) did not bring the balsa wood airplane (clue 2), the plastic one (clue 3), or the paper one (clue 4). His airplane was made of styrofoam.

Knowing this, and the fact that Quincy made the plastic airplane (clue 3), Quincy must be the Ladd child (clue 2—he is not the Smith child). Quincy's airplane was made of plastic. This leaves Rita Smith with the balsa wood airplane.

In Summary:

Patty Bibb - paper   Quincy Ladd - plastic
Sam Cole - styrofoam   Rita Smith - balsa wood

	Bibb	Cole	Ladd	Smith	Styro.	Balsa	Plastic	Paper
Quincy	X	X	O	X	X	X	O	X
Patty	O	X	X	X	X	X	X	O
Rita	X	X	X	O	X	O	X	X
Sam	X	O	X	X	O	X	X	X

ANIMAL ANATOMY (pages 26-27)

1. SNAIL
2. HAMMERHEAD SHARK
3. BOTTLE-NOSE DOLPHIN
4. SMALLMOUTH BASS
5. CHINCHILLA
6. ARMADILLO
7. HUMPBACK WHALE
8. CARIBOU
9. HIPPOPOTAMUS
10. CALF
11. BLACK-FOOTED FERRET
12. THREE-TOED SLOTH

NUMBERS, PLEASE (page 28)

A. 10, 12, 8
B. $2.00, $9.98, $6.00
C. 36, 9, 180
D. 23, 38, 46
E. 8, 45, 350
F. 100, 70, 90
G. 120, 140, 20

STOP, LOOK, AND LIST (page 29)
Here are our answers. You may have found others.

Weather Words	**Things Babies Need**
Dry	Diapers
Sleet	Sleep
Cold	Crib
Misty	Milk
Temperature	Toys

Math Words
Divide
Sum
Calculate
Multiply
Times

LOOKING AROUND THE LIBRARY (pages 30-31)

HORSE SENSE (page 32)

WHAT'S IN A WORD? (page 33)

ail	late	seal	steal
aisle	lease	seat	still
alit	least	sell	tail
all	let	set	tale
ate	lie	sill	tall
ease	list	sit	tease
east	lit	site	tell
eat	little	slat	tie
eel	sail	slate	tile
ill	sale	sleet	till
isle	sat	slit	title
last	sea	stall	

PICTURE MIXER (pages 34-35)

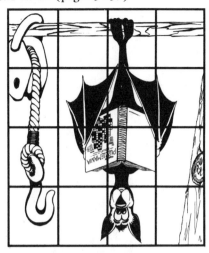

LAST CHANCE WITH "ANCE" (page 37)

1. dance
2. prance
3. trance
4. glance
5. balance
6. entrance
7. allowance
8. allegiance
9. attendance
10. ambulance
11. long distance
12. appliance
13. brilliance
14. acquaintance

WHAT AM I? (page 38)
BEAVER

RAT RACER (page 39)

JOB JUMBLE (pages 40-41)

1. DOCTOR
2. FIRE FIGHTER
3. TEACHER
4. DENTIST
5. GARBAGEMAN
6. PRINCIPAL
7. POLICE OFFICER
8. VETERINARIAN
9. ASTRONAUT
10. ARTIST
11. MAIL CARRIER
12. SAILOR
13. SOLDIER
14. SECRETARY
15. PLUMBER
16. WAITER
17. PAINTER
18. PILOT
19. CLERK
20. CHEF
21. LAWYER
22. CARPENTER
23. MECHANIC
24. WRITER

ROW, ROW, ROW (page 42)

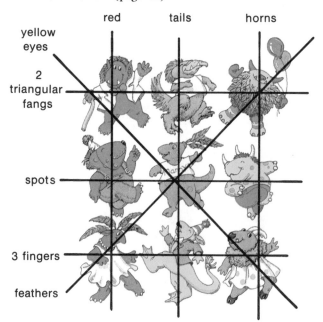

yellow eyes • red • tails • horns

2 triangular fangs

spots

3 fingers

feathers

MUSIC, MUSIC (pages 44-45)

¹C	²O	³R	N	E	T		⁴	⁵H	⁶O	⁷R	N
⁸H	A	Y		X			⁹T	U	B	A	
¹⁰I	R	E			¹¹P	E	R	S	O	N	¹²S
¹³M	S		¹⁴M	A			¹⁵U	K	E		P
E		¹⁶D	I	N		¹⁷M	Y			¹⁸T	I
¹⁹S	²⁰T	A	N	D	U	P		²¹T	O	N	
	²²O	R	E	S		E		²³E	N	E	
²⁴R	E	E	D		²⁵S	T	R	E	E	T	

WAYS TO GO (page 46)

1. airplane (in the words: fair, plan & Edward)
2. ship (in the words: girl's & hip)
3. car (in the words: garlic & arrived)
4. train (in the words: report & rain)
5. horse (in the words: both, or & sell)
6. truck (in the words: Put & rucksacks)
7. boat (in the words: Bobo & at)
8. balloon (in the words: Grab all Oona's)
9. glider (in the words: Greg Liderman)
10. Carriage (in the words: Carri age)

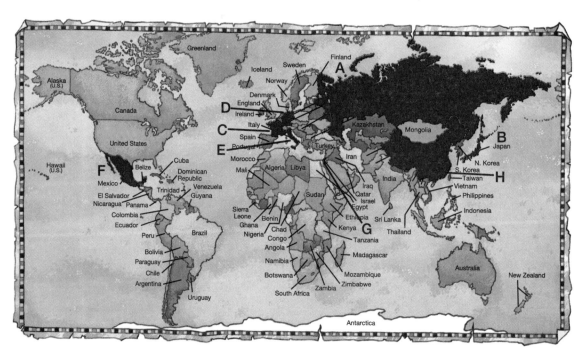

A – 8 Russia – Russian
B – 5 Japan – Japanese
C – 1 France – French
D – 2 Germany – German
E – 3 Italy – Italian
F – 4 Mexico – Spanish
G – 7 Israel – Hebrew
H – 6 China – Chinese

Editor: Jeffrey A. O'Hare • **Art Director:** Timothy J. Gillner • **Project Director:** Pamela Gallo
Editorial Consultant: Andrew Gutelle • **Design Consultant:** Bob Feldgus

Puzzle Contributors
Betty Lou Adamovich • George Anderson • Barbara Backer • Siri Bletzer • Debra Cole • Sheryl Cvijanovich
Mary Fundersberg • Don Hamann • Charles Jordan • Virginia Kroll • Isobel Livingstone • Clare Mishica
Jan Onffroy • Donna Siple • Gary Usinger • Jackie Vaughan • Arlene Wixtrom • Rita Yessick

Bonus Puzzle from MATHMANIA®

PLAYING FOR POINTS

Kim scored half as many points as Chad.

Frank and Carol each scored the same number of points.

Bill had three more points than Kim.

Frank had one more point than Kim.

Bill had eight points.

Chad, Kim, Frank, Carol, and Bill were playing a game. Bill was keeping score, but the dog came in and ran off with the scorepad. Can you help figure out the total number of points scored in this game so far, as well as how many points each player had?

Illustration: R. Michael Palan

ANSWER

Thirty-five points had been scored. Bill had eight, Kim had five, Frank and Carol each had six, and Chad had ten.

Math + Puzzles = FUN!

Here's a sample of the number-crunching fun you'll find in MATHMANIA from Highlights.® With the wide variety of puzzles in MATHMANIA, kids ages 8 and up will enjoy hours of fun.

- Number Codes
- Fun with Shapes
- Coin Puzzles
- Fraction Fun
- Number Squares
- Graph Puzzles
- Logic Games
- "Magic" Math Tricks
- Dot-to-Dots and much more!

Parents: To find out more about the skill-building fun of MATHMANIA and learn about a special offer, call 1-800-962-3661 between 8 a.m. and 9 p.m. EST, Monday through Friday, or visit www.highlightsclubs.com anytime!

$5.95 U.S.
$9.95 Canada

ISBN 0-87534-725-8

50595

9 780875 347257

*Distributed to the trade
by Boyds Mills Press*

Published by
Highlights for Children® Inc.
P.O. Box 18201
Columbus, Ohio 43218-0201

ISBN 0-87534-725-8

Printed in the United States of America

For information on PUZZLEMANIA, visit www.puzzlemania.com or call 1-800-962-3661.

Highlights®
PUZZLEMANIA®

How many differences can you see between these two pictures?

Highlights PUZZLEMANIA®

CONTENTS

CAN YOU FIND . . .

Cover illustration by Dominic Catalano

©1994 Highlights for Children, Inc.
P.O. Box 18201
Columbus, Ohio 43218-0201
www.puzzlemania.com
ISBN 0-87534-749-5

10 9 8 7 6